BRAIN GAMES kids

PRESCHOOL PREP

Illustrations by Martha Avilés, Deborah Colvin Borgo, Robin Boyer, Jane Dippold, Marina Fedotova, Louise Gardner, Daniel Howarth, Agnieszka Jatkowska, Holly Jones, Doug Klauba, Thea Kliros, Sarah Kranz, Barbara Lanza, John Lund, Jane Maday, John Manders, Robert Masheris, David Merrell, Chris Moroney, Burgundy Nilles, Christine Schneider, Susan Spellman, and David Wojtowycz

Photography © Art Explosion, Artville, Brand X, Dreamstime, Fotolia, Image Club, Imagestate, iStock Photo, Jupiter Images Unlimited, Media Bakery, Photodisc, Shutterstock, Stockbyte, StockphotoPro, Thinkstock
Additional photography by Siede Preis Photography and Brian Warling Photography

Customer Service: 1-800-595-8484 or customer_service@pilbooks.com

www.pilbooks.com

p i kids is a trademark of Publications International, Ltd., and is registered in the United States.
Brain Games is a registered trademark of Publications International, Ltd.

8 7 6 5 4 3 2 1

Manufactured in China.

ISBN: 978-1-4508-3982-2

D1410895

publications international

Letter to Parents

Welcome to Brain Games!

Get ready for an exciting kind of early-learning activity! These 301 questions tackle key benchmarks across core categories such as language arts, math, science, social sciences, physical and emotional development, and fine arts. Each left-hand page contains one to four questions; each right-hand page supplies concrete answers. The first section of this book educates and asks questions about letters, numbers, colors, and shapes. The second section of the book contains scattered categories of questions, which progress from easy to hard for a graduated learning experience. Colorful illustrations and photography help present the material in a fun and engaging way. Settle down, open the book, and have fun learning with your child today!

How to Use

- Open to the desired set of questions and answers. Fold the book in half so you and your child see only the questions.

- Read the questions aloud. Ask your child to point to or name the answer.

- Flip the book over to reveal the answers. The answers are shown in red. Miss a few? Don't worry! Every child develops a little differently—go back and try these questions again in a few days or even months. Build confidence and continue at a pace that is comfortable for your child.

Some Tips

- Your child might not be familiar with all of the content on these pages. Take the time to introduce new concepts and characters when these kinds of questions come up.

- Encourage an older sibling or friend to share this Q&A time. Take turns asking the child questions. The older child just might learn something, too.

- Be positive and encouraging. Learning should be fun! When your child seems tired, frustrated, or unfocused, take a break. You can always play again later.

Questions

What is this letter?
Trace it with your finger.

What is this animal?

What is this?
What is its first letter?

Point to the things that
begin with the letter **A**.

Answers

5

What is this letter?
Trace it with your finger.

This is the letter A.

What is this animal?
Alligator

What is this?
What is its first letter?
Acorn begins with the letter A.

Point to the things that begin with the letter **A**.

Alligator

Acorn

Questions

What is this letter?
Trace it with your finger.

B

What floats on the water?

What is the first letter
of this flying bug?

Point to the things that
begin with the letter **B**.

What is this letter?
Trace it with your finger.

2

This is the letter B.

What floats on the water?

Boat

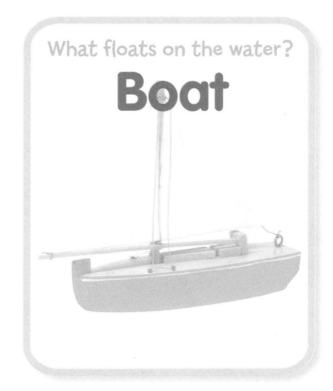

What is the first letter
of this flying bug?

**Bee begins with
the letter B.**

Point to the things that
begin with the letter **B.**

Bee

Boat

What is this letter?
Trace it with your finger.

What is this bird?

What is this?
What is its first letter?

Point to the things that begin with the letter C.

What is this letter?
Trace it with your finger.

C

This is the letter C.

What is this bird?
Chicken

What is this?
What is its first letter?
Clock begins with the letter C.

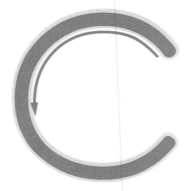

Point to the things that begin with the letter C.

Clock

Chicken

Questions

What is this letter?
Trace it with your finger.

D

What is this animal?

What is this?
What is its first letter?

Point to the things that
begin with the letter D.

What is this letter?
Trace it with your finger.

2

This is the letter D.

What is this animal?

Deer

What is this?
What is its first letter?
**Door begins with
the letter D.**

Point to the things that
begin with the letter **D**.

Deer   **Door**

What is this letter? Trace it with your finger.

E

What do we see with?

What is the first letter of this animal with a trunk?

Point to the things that begin with the letter **E**.

What is this letter?
Trace it with your finger.

E
2
3
4

This is the letter E.

What do we see with?

Eyes

What is the first letter of this animal with a trunk?

Elephant begins with the letter E.

Point to the things that begin with the letter E.

Elephant

Eyes

Questions

What is this letter?
Trace it with your finger.

F

Who takes care of
barnyard animals?

What is the first letter
of this green animal?

Point to the things that
begin with the letter **F**.

What is this letter?
Trace it with your finger.

F
2
3

This is the letter F.

Who takes care of
barnyard animals?

Farmer

What is the first letter
of this green animal?

**Frog begins with
the letter F.**

Point to the things that
begin with the letter **F**.

Frog

Farmer

Questions

What is this letter? Trace it with your finger.

G

What is this big animal?

What is the first letter of this musical instrument?

Point to the things that begin with the letter G.

What is this letter?
Trace it with your finger.

This is the letter G.

What is this big animal?

Gorilla

What is the first letter of
this musical instrument?

**Guitar begins with
the letter G.**

Point to the things that
begin with the letter **G.**

Guitar

Gorilla

Questions

What is this letter?
Trace it with your finger.

H

What is this body part?

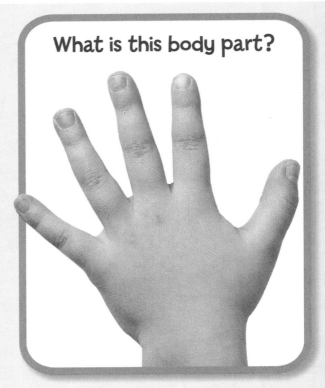

What is the first letter
of this tool?

Point to the things that
begin with the letter **H**.

What is this letter?
Trace it with your finger.

This is the letter H.

What is this body part?

Hand

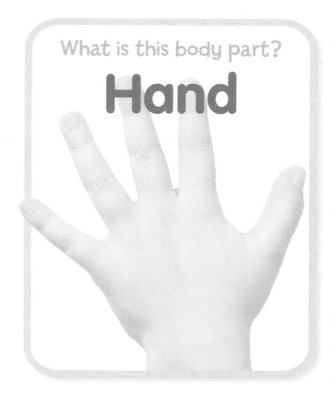

What is the first letter
of this tool?

**Hammer begins
with the letter H.**

Point to the things that
begin with the letter H.

Hand

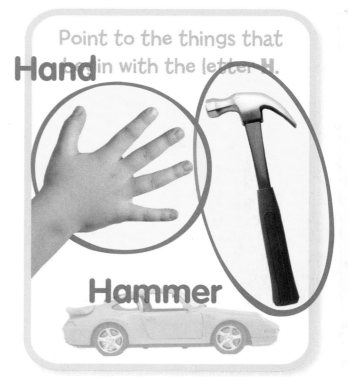

Hammer

Questions

What is this letter?
Trace it with your finger.

I

What is a house made of snow called?

What is this?
What is its first letter?

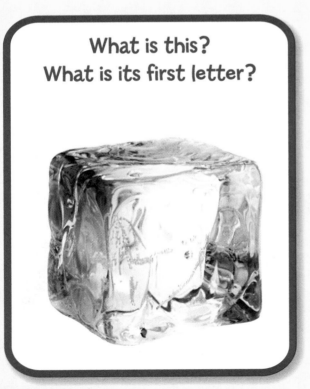

Point to the things that begin with the letter I.

What is this letter?
Trace it with your finger.

This is the letter I.

What is a house made
of snow called?

Igloo

What is this?
What is its first letter?

**Ice begins
with the letter I.**

Point to the things that
begin with the letter **I.**

Igloo

Ice

Questions

What is this letter?
Trace it with your finger.

J

What is this sea creature?

What is the first letter
of this toy?

Point to the things that
begin with the letter **J**.

What is this letter? Trace it with your finger.

2↓ J→

This is the letter J.

What is this sea creature?

Jellyfish

What is the first letter of this toy?

Jump rope begins with the letter J.

Point to the things that begin with the letter J.

Jellyfish

Jump rope

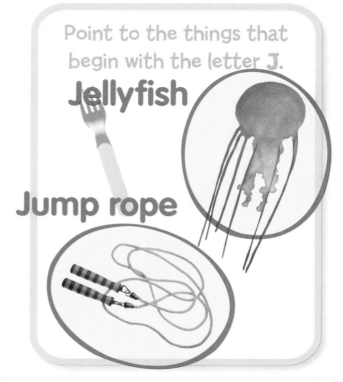

What is this letter?
Trace it with your finger.

K

What unlocks things?

What is the first letter
of this animal?

Point to the things that
begin with the letter **K**.

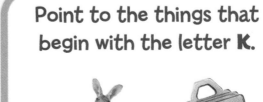

What is this letter?
Trace it with your finger.

This is the letter K.

What unlocks things?

Key

What is the first letter
of this animal?

**Kangaroo begins
with the letter K.**

Point to the things that
begin with the letter **K.**

Kangaroo

Key

What is this letter?
Trace it with your finger.

L

What is this animal?

What is the first letter
of this sour fruit?

Point to the things that
begin with the letter **L**.

What is this letter?
Trace it with your finger.

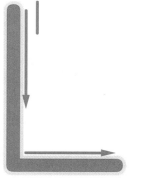

This is the letter L.

What is this animal?
Lion

What is the first letter of this sour fruit?

Lemon begins with the letter L.

Point to the things that begin with the letter L.

Lion

Lemon

What is this letter?
Trace it with your finger.

M

What animal likes cheese?

What is the first letter
of this silly animal?

Point to the things that
begin with the letter **M**.

What is this letter?
Trace it with your finger.

This is the letter M.

What animal likes cheese?

Mouse

What is the first letter
of this silly animal?

**Monkey begins with
the letter M.**

Point to the things that
begin with the letter **M**.

Mouse

Monkey

What is this letter?
Trace it with your finger.

Where do birds live?

What is this?
What is its first letter?

Point to the things that
begin with the letter N.

What is this letter?
Trace it with your finger.

This is the letter N.

Where do birds live?

Nest

What is this?
What is its first letter?

Net begins with the letter N.

Point to the things that begin with the letter N.

Net

Nest

Questions

**What is this letter?
Trace it with your finger.**

What is this sea animal?

**What is the first letter
of this vegetable?**

**Point to the things that
begin with the letter O.**

What is this letter? Trace it with your finger.

This is the letter O.

What is this sea animal?

Octopus

What is the first letter of this vegetable?

Onion begins with the letter O.

Point to the things that begin with the letter O.

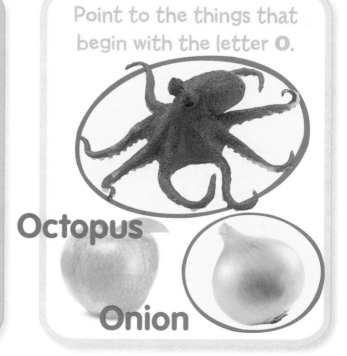

Octopus

Onion

Questions

What is this letter?
Trace it with your finger.

P

What can you write with?

What is the first letter
of this yummy food?

Point to the things that
begin with the letter **P**.

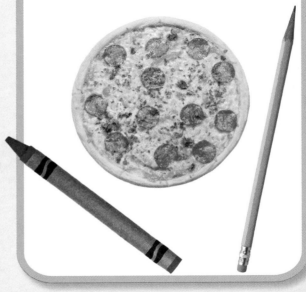

What is this letter?
Trace it with your finger.

P 2

This is the letter P.

What can you write with?

Pencil

What is the first letter
of this yummy food?

**Pizza begins with
the letter P.**

Point to the things that
begin with the letter **P**.

Pizza

Pencil

What is this letter?
Trace it with your finger.

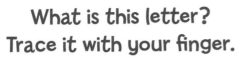

Who wears a crown?

What is the first letter
of this symbol?

Point to the things that
begin with the letter Q.

What is this letter?
Trace it with your finger.

This is the letter Q.

Who wears a crown?

Queen

What is the first letter
of this symbol?

**Question mark
begins with the
letter Q.**

Point to the things that
begin with the letter Q.

Queen   **Question
mark**

What is this letter?
Trace it with your finger.

R

What jewelry is worn
on a finger?

What is the first letter
of this weather?

Point to the things that
begin with the letter **R**.

What is this letter?
Trace it with your finger.

R
2

This is the letter R.

What jewelry is worn
on a finger?

Ring

What is the first letter
of this weather?

**Rain begins with
the letter R.**

Point to the things that
begin with the letter R.

Rain

Ring

What is this letter? Trace it with your finger.

S

What do we wear on our feet?

What is the first letter of this tool?

Point to the things that begin with the letter **S**.

What is this letter?
Trace it with your finger.

This is the letter S.

What do we wear on our feet?
Socks

What is the first letter of this tool?
Saw begins with the letter S.

Point to the things that begin with the letter S.

Socks

Saw

Questions

What is this letter?
Trace it with your finger.

T

What is this?

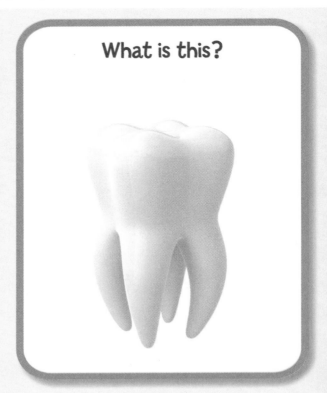

What is the first letter of
this animal with a shell?

Point to the things that
begin with the letter **T**.

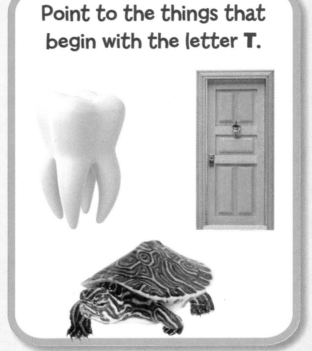

What is this letter?
Trace it with your finger.

2

This is the letter T.

What is this?

Tooth

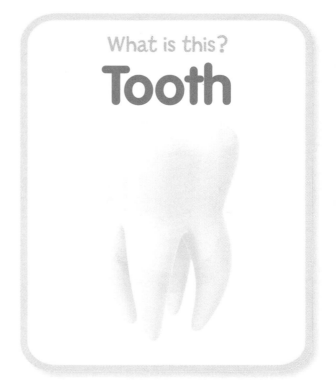

What is the first letter of this animal with a shell?
Turtle begins with the letter T.

Point to the things that begin with the letter **T**.

Tooth

Turtle

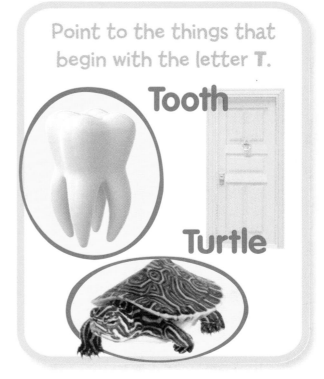

Questions

What is this letter?
Trace it with your finger.

U

What is this magical animal?

What is the first letter of this object?

Point to the things that begin with the letter **U**.

What is this letter?
Trace it with your finger.

This is the letter U.

What is this magical animal?

Unicorn

What is the first letter
of this object?

**Umbrella begins with
the letter U.**

Point to the things that
begin with the letter **U.**

Unicorn

Umbrella

Questions

What is this letter?
Trace it with your finger.

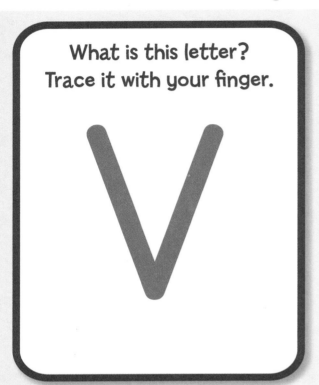

Where does lava come from?

What is the first letter
of this instrument?

Point to the things that
begin with the letter **V**.

Answers

What is this letter?
Trace it with your finger.

This is the letter V.

Where does lava come from?

Volcano

What is the first letter
of this instrument?
**Violin begins with
the letter V.**

Point to the things that
begin with the letter **V**.

Violin

Volcano

What is this letter?
Trace it with your finger.

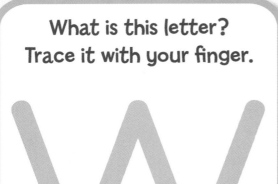

What is this animal that
swims in the water?

What is the first letter
of this juicy fruit?

Point to the things that
begin with the letter **W**.

What is this letter?
Trace it with your finger.

This is the letter W.

What is this animal that
swims in the water?

Whale

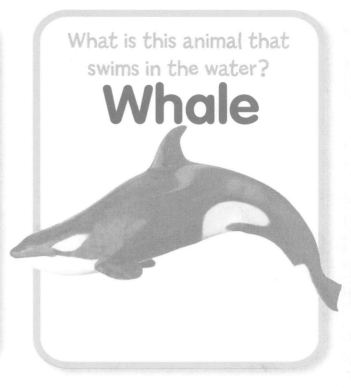

What is the first letter
of this juicy fruit?

**Watermelon begins
with the letter W.**

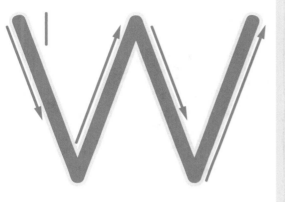

Point to the things that
begin with the letter **W**.

Watermelon

Whale

Questions

What is this letter? Trace it with your finger.

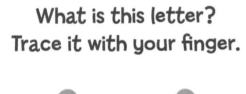

What is this instrument?

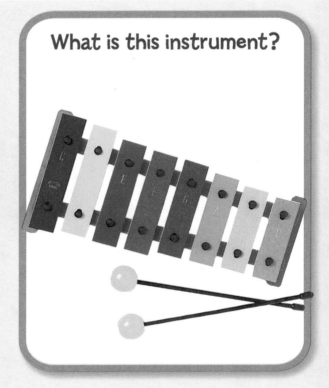

What is the first letter of this image?

Point to the things that begin with the letter X.

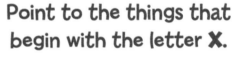

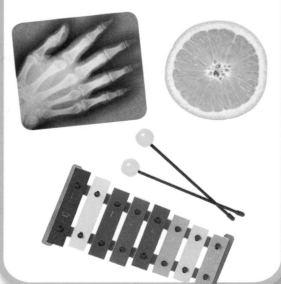

What is this letter?
Trace it with your finger.

1 X 2

This is the letter X.

What is this instrument?
Xylophone

What is the first letter of this image?
X-ray begins with the letter X.

Point to the things that begin with the letter X.

X-ray

Xylophone

What is this letter? Trace it with your finger.

Y

What do we do when we are sleepy?

What is the first letter of this healthy snack?

Point to the things that begin with the letter y.

What is this letter?
Trace it with your finger.

This is the letter Y.

What do we do when
we are sleepy?

Yawn

What is the first letter
of this healthy snack?
**Yogurt begins with
the letter Y.**

Point to the things that
begin with the letter **y.**

Yogurt

Yawn

What is this letter?
Trace it with your finger.

Z

What is sometimes
on a jacket?

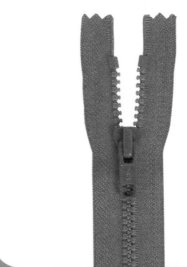

What is the first letter
of this animal?

Point to the things that
begin with the letter **Z**.

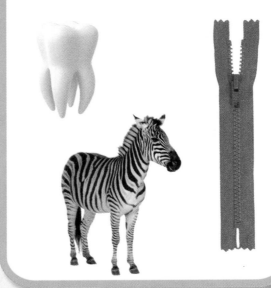

Answers

What is this letter?
Trace it with your finger.

This is the letter Z.

What is sometimes
on a jacket?
Zipper

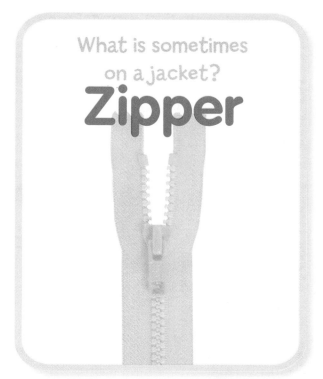

What is the first letter
of this animal?
**Zebra begins with
the letter Z.**

Point to the things that
begin with the letter **Z**.
Zipper

Zebra

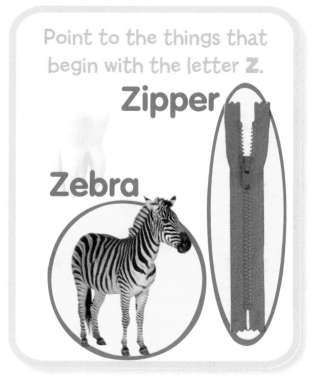

Question

Sing the Alphabet Song, then answer the question.

A B _ _ D E F G
H I J K
L M _ _ O P
Q R S
T U _ _
W X Y Z

Now I know my ABCs! Next time, won't you sing with me?

What letters are missing?

Sing the Alphabet Song, then answer the question.

A B C D E F G
H I J K
L M N O P
Q R S
T U V
W X Y Z

Now I know my ABCs! Next time, won't you sing with me?

What letters are missing?

Questions

What is this number?
Trace it with your finger.

1

What number is missing?

_23

How many balloons do you see?

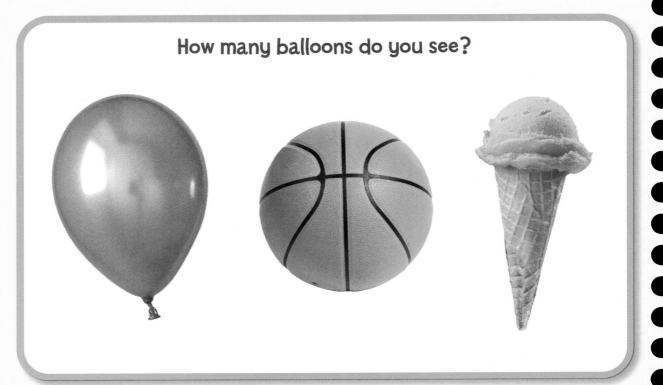

What is this number?
Trace it with your finger.

This is the number 1.

What number is missing?

1 2 3

How many balloons do you see?

Questions

What is this number? Trace it with your finger.

2

What number is missing?

1 _ 3

How many shoes do you see?

What is this number?
Trace it with your finger.

2

This is the number 2.

What number is missing?

1 **2** 3

How many shoes do you see?

2

62

Questions

What is this number?
Trace it with your finger.

3

What number is missing?

12_

How many pennies can you count?

What is this number? Trace it with your finger.

3

This is the number 3.

What number is missing?

1 2 3

How many pennies can you count?

3

**What is this number?
Trace it with your finger.**

4

What number comes next?

2 3 ___

**How many fish
do you see?**

What is this number?
Trace it with your finger.

This is the number 4.

What number comes next?

2 3 4

How many fish
do you see?

Questions

What is this number?
Trace it with your finger.

5

What number is next?

3 4 _

How many kittens are there?

What is this number?
Trace it with your finger.

5

This is the number 5.

What number is next?

3 4 5

How many kittens are there?

5

Questions

What is this number?
Trace it with your finger.

6

How many leaves
do you see?

What number is missing?

4   5   ?

What is this number?
Trace it with your finger.

This is the number 6.

What number is missing?

4   5   ⑥

How many leaves do you see?

70

Questions

What is this number? Trace it with your finger.

7

What number is missing?

How many flowers do you see?

What is this number?
Trace it with your finger.

7

This is the number 7.

What number is missing?

8
7
6

How many flowers do you see?

7

Questions

What is this number? Trace it with your finger.

8

What number is next?

How many dots are on the dominoes?

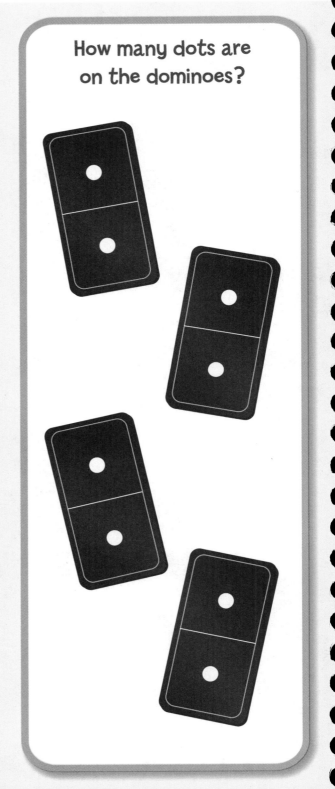

Answers

What is this number?
Trace it with your finger.

This is the number 8.

What number is next?

How many dots are
on the dominoes?

8

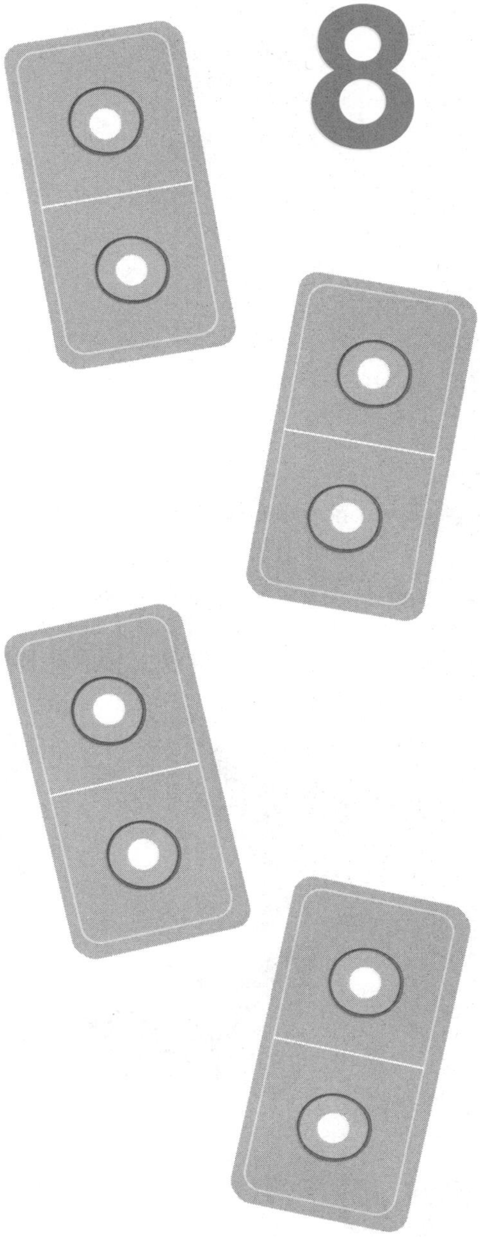

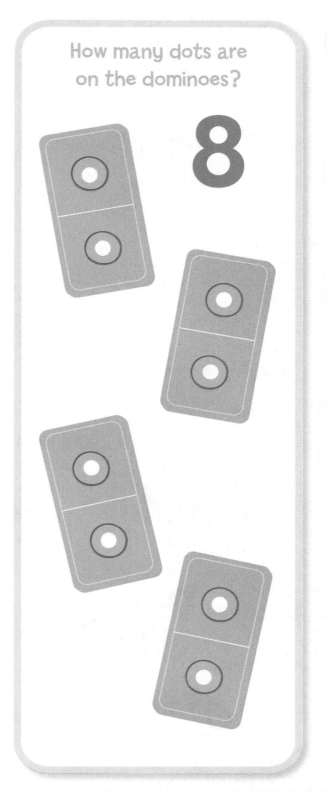

Questions

What is this number? Trace it with your finger.

9

What number is missing?

8 ___ 10

How many butterflies do you see?

What is this number? Trace it with your finger.

This is the number 9.

What number is missing?

8 9 10

How many butterflies do you see?

9

Questions

What is this number? Trace it with your finger.

10

What number is next?

8   9

How many apples can you count?

What is this number?
Trace it with your finger.

10

This is the number 10.

What number is next?

8 9 10

How many apples
can you count?

10

Questions

What is this number? Trace it with your finger.

11

What number is missing?

How many trucks do you see?

Answers

What is this number? Trace it with your finger.

This is the number 11.

What number is missing?

How many trucks do you see?

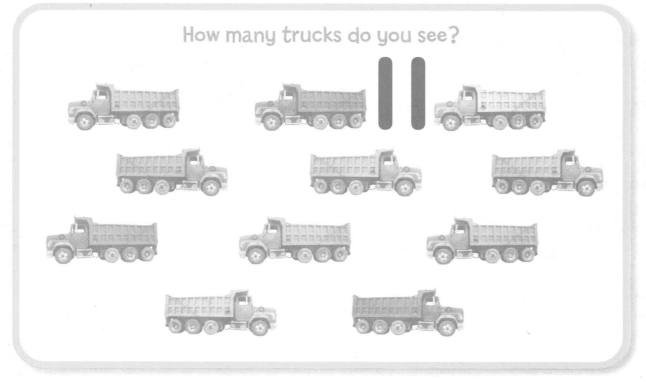

Questions

What is this number? Trace it with your finger.

12

What number is missing?

How many bees are there?

What is this number?
Trace it with your finger.

12

This is the number 12.

What number is missing?

How many bees
are there?

Questions

What is this number?
Trace it with your finger.

13

What number is next?

How many cars do you see?

What is this number?
Trace it with your finger.

This is the number 13.

What number is next?

How many cars do you see?

Questions

What is this number?
Trace it with your finger.

14

What number is next?

11   12

13   ___

How many books
do you count?

What is this number?
Trace it with your finger.

This is the number 14.

What number is next?

11 12

13 **14**

How many books do you count?

Questions

What is this number?
Trace it with your finger.

15

What number is next?

13 14 ___

How many puppies do you see?

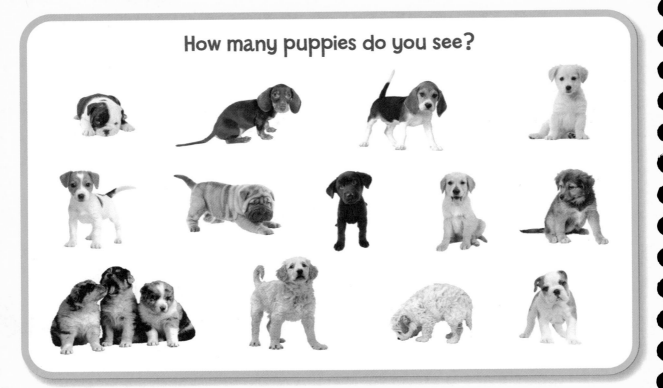

What is this number?
Trace it with your finger.

This is the number 15.

What number is next?

How many puppies do you see?

Questions

What color is this rose?

Which one is red?

What color is the frog?

Which one is green?

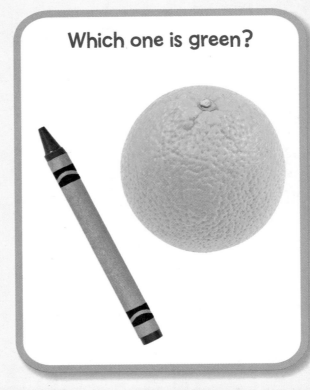

What color is this rose?

Red

Trace the word with your finger.

Which one is red?

What color is the frog?

Green

Trace the word with your finger.

Which one is green?

Questions

What color is the juice?

Which one is orange?

What color is the jelly?

Which one is purple?

What color is the juice?

Orange

Trace the word with your finger.

Which one is orange?

What color is the jelly?

Purple

Trace the word with your finger.

Which one is purple?

Questions

What color are the mailboxes?

Which one is blue?

What color is the cheese?

Which one is yellow?

What color are
the mailboxes?

Blue

**Trace the word
with your finger.**

Which one is blue?

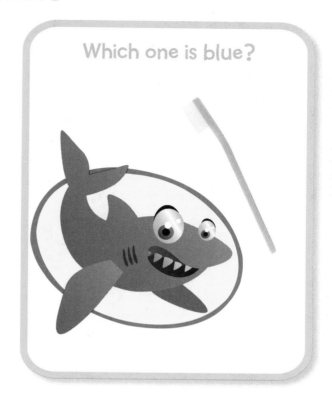

What color is the cheese?

Yellow

**Trace the word
with your finger.**

Which one is yellow?

94

Questions

What color is the baseball bat?

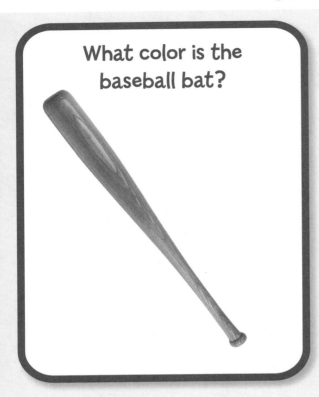

Which one is brown?

What color is the puppy?

Which one is black?

What color is the baseball bat?

Brown

Trace the word with your finger.

Which one is brown?

What color is the puppy?

Black

Trace the word with your finger.

Which one is black?

Questions

What color is the ice cream?

Which one is pink?

What color is the bunny?

Which one is white?

What color is the ice cream?

Pink

Trace the word with your finger.

Which one is pink?

What color is the bunny?

White

Trace the word with your finger.

Which one is white?

Questions

What is this shape?
Trace it with your finger.

Which one is a diamond?

What is this shape?
Trace it with your finger.

Which one is a triangle?

What is this shape?
Trace it with your finger.

Diamond

Which one is a diamond?

What is this shape?
Trace it with your finger.

Triangle

Which one is a triangle?

Questions

**What is this shape?
Trace it with your finger.**

Which one is an oval?

**What is this shape?
Trace it with your finger.**

Which one is a circle?

What is this shape?
Trace it with your finger.

Oval

Which one is an oval?

What is this shape?
Trace it with your finger.

Circle

Which one is a circle?

What is this shape?
Trace it with your finger.

Which one is a heart?

What is this shape?
Trace it with your finger.

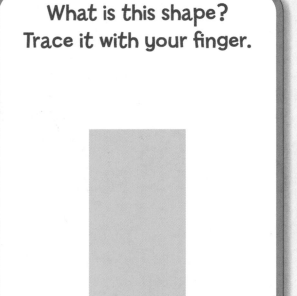

Which one is a rectangle?

What is this shape?
Trace it with your finger.

Heart

Which one is a heart?

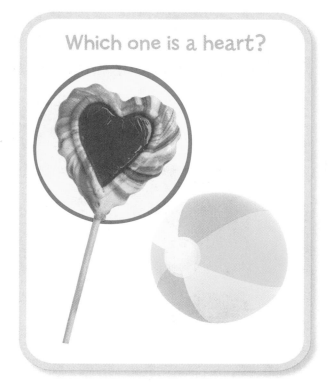

What is this shape?
Trace it with your finger.

Rectangle

Which one is a rectangle?

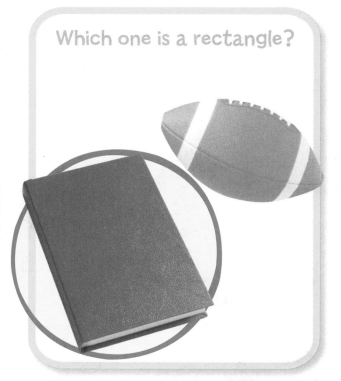

Questions

What is this shape? Trace it with your finger.

Which one is a square?

What is this shape? Trace it with your finger.

Which is a star?

What is this shape?
Trace it with your finger.

Square

Which one is a square?

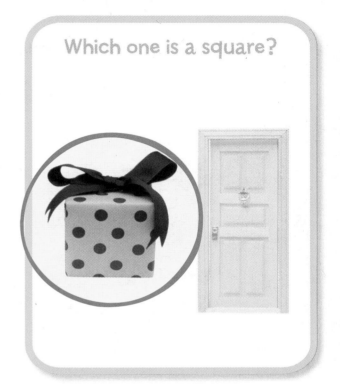

What is this shape?
Trace it with your finger.

Star

Which is a star?

Read the nursery rhyme, then answer the question.

This Little Piggy

This little piggy
went to market.

This little piggy
stayed home.

This little piggy
had roast beef.

This little piggy
had none.

This little piggy cried, "Wee-wee-wee!"
All they way home.

How many little piggies were there?

Read the nursery rhyme, then answer the question.

This Little Piggy

This little piggy
went to market.

This little piggy
stayed home.

This little piggy
had roast beef.

This little piggy
had none.

There were 5 little piggies.

This little piggy cried, "Wee-wee-wee!"
All they way home.

How many little piggies were there?

Questions

Who is mad?

Which animal is a fox?

When there is snow on the ground and it's cold outside, what should we wear?

Who is mad?

Which animal is a fox?

When there is snow on the ground and it's cold outside, what should we wear?

Sing the song, then answer the question.

Old MacDonald

Old MacDonald had a farm, E-I-E-I-O.
On his farm he had some cows, E-I-E-I-O.
With a moo-moo here and a moo-moo there,
Here a moo, there a moo, everywhere a moo-moo.
Old MacDonald had a farm, E-I-E-I-O.

What did the cows say on Old MacDonald's farm?

Sing the song, then answer the question.

Old MacDonald

Old MacDonald had a farm, E-I-E-I-O.
On his farm he had some cows, E-I-E-I-O.
With a moo-moo here and a moo-moo there,
Here a moo, there a moo, everywhere a moo-moo.
Old MacDonald had a farm, E-I-E-I-O.

The cows said moo.

What did the cows say on Old MacDonald's farm?

Questions

What body parts help us walk?

What do we say when we get a treat?

What is this animal?

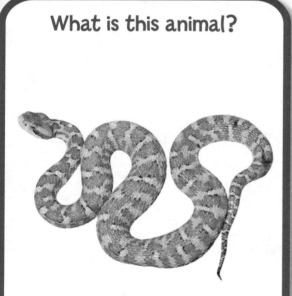

Which one is a fruit?

What body parts
help us walk?

Feet

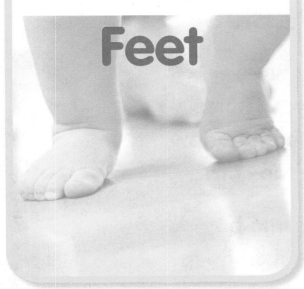

What do we say when
we get a treat?

Thank you

What is this animal?

Snake

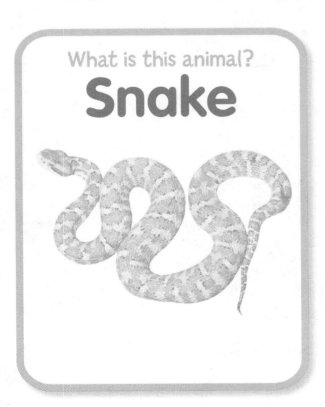

Which one is a fruit?

Orange

Read the nursery rhyme, then answer the question.

Little Boy Blue

Little Boy Blue,
Come blow your horn.
The sheep's in the meadow,
The cow's in the corn.

Where's the little boy
Who looks after the sheep?
Under the haystack
Fast asleep.

What did Little Boy Blue blow?

Read the nursery rhyme, then answer the question.

Little Boy Blue

Little Boy Blue,
Come blow your horn.
The sheep's in the meadow,
The cow's in the corn.

Where's the little boy
Who looks after the sheep?
Under the haystack
Fast asleep.

Little Boy Blue blew his horn.

What did Little Boy Blue blow?

Questions

How do we politely ask for something?

What is this animal?

What do we do with this?

How many feet do we have?

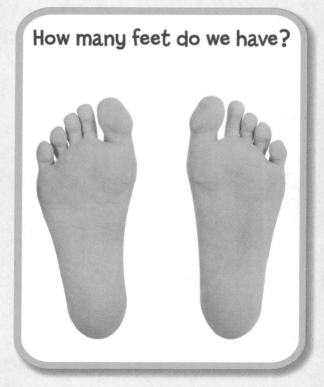

How do we politely ask for something?

Please

What is this animal?

Ostrich

What do we do with this?

Wash

What do we do with this?

How many feet do we have?

2

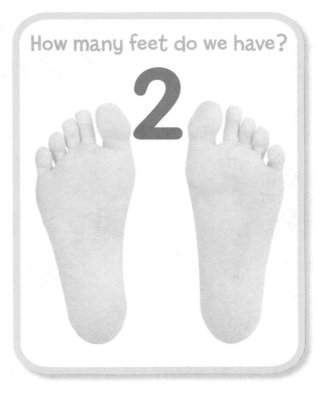

Sing the song, then answer the question.

On Top of Spaghetti

**On top of spaghetti,
All covered with cheese.
I lost my poor meatball,
When somebody sneezed.**

What was the spaghetti covered with?

Sing the song, then answer the question.

On Top of Spaghetti

On top of spaghetti,
All covered with cheese.
I lost my poor meatball,
When somebody sneezed.

The spaghetti was covered with cheese.

What was the spaghetti covered with?

120

Questions

What part of the body do we use to see?

What does a bird use to fly?

Which one is a vegetable?

What do we say if we accidentally burp?

What part of the body do we use to see?

Eyes

What does a bird use to fly?

Wings

Which one is a vegetable?

Broccoli

What do we say if we accidentally burp?

Excuse me

Read the story, then answer the question.

Little Red Riding Hood

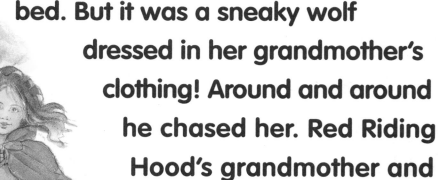

One day, Little Red Riding Hood's mother asked her to deliver treats to her sick grandmother. When Red Riding Hood arrived, she found her grandmother in bed. But it was a sneaky wolf dressed in her grandmother's clothing! Around and around he chased her. Red Riding Hood's grandmother and a kind woodsman saved her from the hungry wolf.

Where was Little Red Riding Hood going?

Read the story, then answer the question.

Little Red Riding Hood

One day, Little Red Riding Hood's mother asked her to deliver treats to her sick grandmother. When Red Riding Hood arrived, she found her grandmother in bed. But it was a sneaky wolf dressed in her grandmother's clothing! Around and around he chased her. Red Riding Hood's grandmother and a kind woodsman saved her from the hungry wolf.

Where was Red Riding Hood going?

She was going to her grandmother's house.

Questions

When it rains, what should we wear?

What do we do with this?

What is the opposite of slow?

SLOW **?** _____

When it rains, what should we wear?

Raincoat

What do we do with this?

Brush our teeth.

What is the opposite of slow?

SLOW

FAST

Read the story, then answer the question.

Jack and the Beanstalk

Once there was a boy named Jack who sold a cow for some magic beans. When Jack brought the beans home, his mom threw them out the window. The next day there was a huge beanstalk! Jack climbed up the beanstalk and found a giant who had lots of riches. Jack brought the treasures home to his mother.

Who lived at the top of the beanstalk?

Read the story, then answer the question.

Jack and the Beanstalk

Once there was a boy named Jack who sold a cow for some magic beans. When Jack brought the beans home, his mom threw them out the window. The next day there was a huge beanstalk! Jack climbed up the beanstalk and found a giant who had lots of riches. Jack brought the treasures home to his mother.

Who lived at the top of the beanstalk?

A giant lived at the top of the beanstalk.

Questions

How many legs does
a dog have?

What should you do
when you cough?

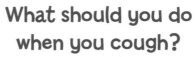

Who is surprised?

What is this part
of the body?

How many legs does a dog have?

4

What should you do when you cough?

Cover your mouth.

Who is surprised?

What is this part of the body?

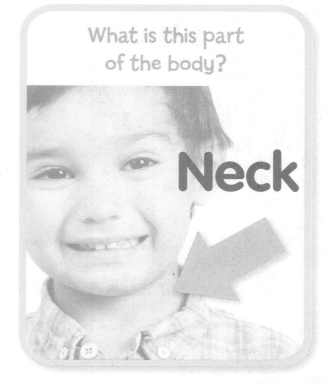

Neck

Read the nursery rhyme, then answer the question.

Eeny, Meeny, Miny, Moe

Eeny, meeny, miny, moe,
Catch a tiger by the toe.
If it hollers let him go,
Eeny, meeny, miny, moe!

Which animal is a tiger?

Read the nursery rhyme, then answer the question.

Eeny, Meeny, Miny, Moe

Eeny, meeny, miny, moe,
Catch a tiger by the toe.
If it hollers let him go,
Eeny, meeny, miny, moe!

Which animal is a tiger?

Questions

What is the opposite of big?

BIG

?

When plants start to grow, what season is it?

How many hands does a person have?

What animal is this?

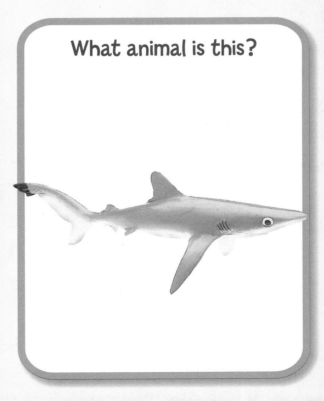

What is the opposite of big?

BIG

LITTLE

When plants start to grow, what season is it?

Spring

How many hands does a person have?

2

What animal is this?

Shark

Read the story, then answer the question.

Cinderella

Cinderella had a mean stepmother and two mean stepsisters. They made her do all the chores. One day there was a royal ball, and Cinderella couldn't go. With the help of a fairy godmother, Cinderella arrived at the ball in a beautiful gown. She met the prince and the two lived happily ever after.

Who helped Cinderella?

Read the story, then answer the question.

Cinderella

Cinderella had a mean stepmother and two mean stepsisters. They made her do all the chores. One day there was a royal ball, and Cinderella couldn't go. With the help of a fairy godmother, Cinderella arrived at the ball in a beautiful gown. She met the prince and the two lived happily ever after.

Her fairy godmother helped her.

Who helped Cinderella?

Which animal says meow?

Which one is a fruit?

Where do we take a bath?

What is this part of the face?

Which animal says meow?

Cat

Which one is a fruit?

Banana

Where do we take a bath?

What is this part of the face?

Chin

Sing the song, then answer the question.

Yankee Doodle

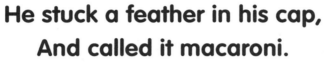

Yankee Doodle went to town,
Riding on a pony.
He stuck a feather in his cap,
And called it macaroni.
Yankee Doodle, keep it up
Yankee Doodle dandy.
Mind the music and the step
And with the girls be handy.

What did Yankee Doodle ride?

Sing the song, then answer the question.

Yankee Doodle

Yankee Doodle went to town,
Riding on a pony.
He stuck a feather in his cap,
And called it macaroni.
Yankee Doodle, keep it up
Yankee Doodle dandy.
Mind the music and the step
And with the girls be handy.

He rode a pony.

What did Yankee Doodle ride?

Questions

What should we say when we see someone?

Who is happy?

What is this part of the body?

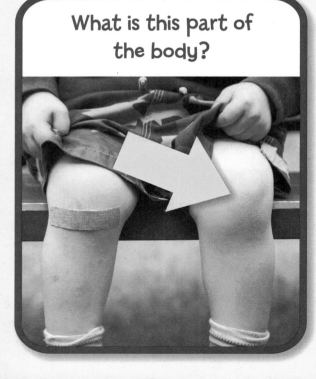

Which animal flies?

What should we say when we see someone?

Hello

Who is happy?

What is this part of the body?

Knee

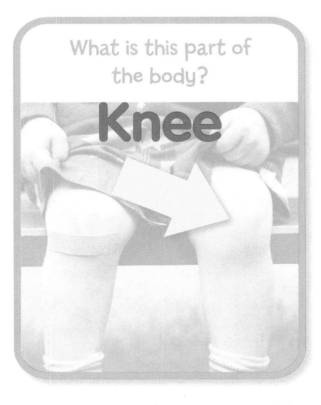

Which animal flies?

Bird

Read the story, then answer the question.

Rip Van Winkle

One day, Rip Van Winkle went for a walk in the mountains. He met a magical troll and became very tired. He settled down for a nap. But Rip Van Winkle fell asleep for 20 years! When he woke up, he had long hair and no one recognized him. But in the end, he was able to find his friends and family.

How long did Rip Van Winkle sleep?

Read the story, then answer the question.

Rip Van Winkle

One day, Rip Van Winkle went for a walk in the mountains. He met a magical troll and became very tired. He settled down for a nap. But Rip Van Winkle fell asleep for 20 years! When he woke up, he had long hair and no one recognized him. But in the end, he was able to find his friends and family.

20 Years

How long did Rip Van Winkle sleep?

Questions

What is this part of the arm called?

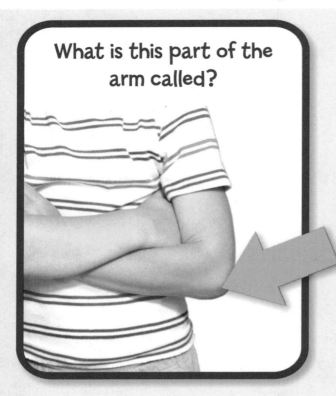

Which one is a zebra?

What is the opposite of short?

?

SHORT

What part of the body do we hear things with?

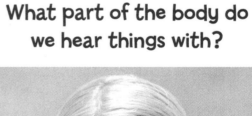

Answers

What is this part of the arm called?

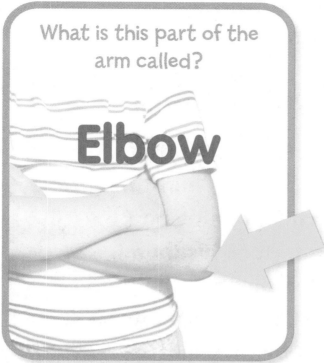

Elbow

Which one is a zebra?

What is the opposite of short?

TALL

SHORT

What part of the body do we hear things with?

Ears

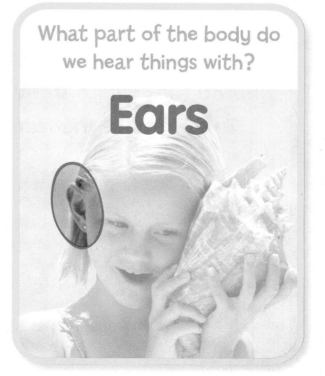

Sing the song, then answer the question.

The Ants Go Marching

The ants go marching one by one, hurrah, hurrah!
The ants go marching one by one, hurrah, hurrah!
The ants go marching one by one,
The little one stops to suck his thumb,
And they all go marching down to the ground
To get out of the rain, BOOM! BOOM! BOOM!
The ants go marching two by two, hurrah, hurrah!
The ants go marching two by two, hurrah, hurrah!
The ants go marching two by two,
The little one stops to tie his shoe,
And they all go marching down to the ground
To get out of the rain, BOOM! BOOM! BOOM!

How many purple ants do you see?

Sing the song, then answer the question.

The Ants Go Marching

The ants go marching one by one, hurrah, hurrah!
The ants go marching one by one, hurrah, hurrah!
The ants go marching one by one,
The little one stops to suck his thumb,
And they all go marching down to the ground
To get out of the rain, BOOM! BOOM! BOOM!
The ants go marching two by two, hurrah, hurrah!
The ants go marching two by two, hurrah, hurrah!
The ants go marching two by two,
The little one stops to tie his shoe,
And they all go marching down to the ground
To get out of the rain, BOOM! BOOM! BOOM!

How many purple ants do you see?

3

Question

Read the story, then answer the question.

Sleeping Beauty

One day, a princess pricked her finger and fell asleep. It was a spell from an evil witch! Everyone in the kingdom tried to wake her, but no one could. Then one day a prince came, having heard about the princess. His love for her broke the spell! The kingdom celebrated and the prince and princess lived happily ever after.

Who woke Sleeping Beauty?

Read the story, then answer the question.

Sleeping Beauty

One day, a princess pricked her finger and fell asleep. It was a spell from an evil witch! Everyone in the kingdom tried to wake her, but no one could. Then one day a prince came, having heard about the princess. His love for her broke the spell! The kingdom celebrated and the prince and princess lived happily ever after.

A prince woke her.

Who woke Sleeping Beauty?

Questions

Which animal lives in the cold?

What do we use to comb our hair?

What is this part of the body called?

What is the opposite of sad?

SAD _____ **?**

Answers

151

Which animal lives in the cold?

Polar bear

What do we use to comb our hair?

Comb

What is this part of the body called?

Shoulder

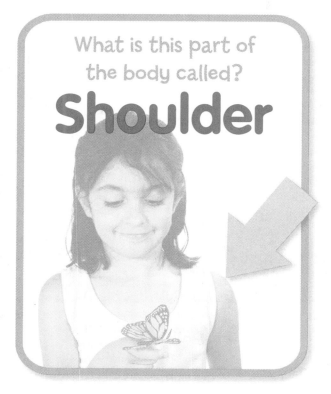

What is the opposite of sad?

SAD HAPPY

Read the story, then answer the question.

Hansel and Gretel

Hansel and Gretel wandered off into the woods one day. Hansel left a trail of breadcrumbs so they could find their way back. But birds ate the crumbs! Hansel and Gretel found a cottage made of candy. But it belonged to a witch! Luckily they were able to escape and find their way back home.

What did Hansel use to make a path?

Read the story, then answer the question.

Hansel and Gretel

Hansel and Gretel wandered off into the woods one day. Hansel left a trail of breadcrumbs so they could find their way back. But birds ate the crumbs! Hansel and Gretel found a cottage made of candy. But it belonged to a witch! Luckily they were able to escape and find their way back home.

He used breadcrumbs.

What did Hansel use to make a path?

Questions

Which animal lives in the water?

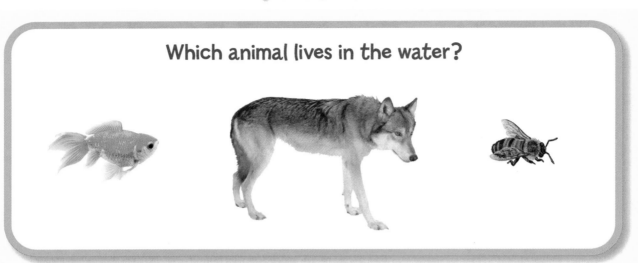

Who is sad?

Which one is a vegetable?

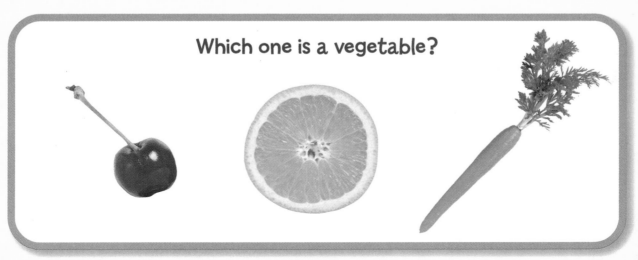

Answers

Which animal lives in the water?

Fish

Who is sad?

Which one is a vegetable?

Carrot

Read the story, then answer the question.

Three Little Pigs

Once there were 3 little pigs. One built a house of straw, one built a house of sticks, and one built a house of bricks. One day a wolf came to all three houses. He blew down the house of straw and the house of sticks! But when he tried to blow the brick house down, he couldn't. The last pig had outsmarted the wolf!

What did the last pig build his house with?

Read the story, then answer the question.

Three Little Pigs

Once there were 3 little pigs. One built a house of straw, one built a house of sticks, and one built a house of bricks. One day a wolf came to all three houses. He blew down the house of straw and the house of sticks! But when he tried to blow the brick house down, he couldn't. The last pig had outsmarted the wolf!

He built his house with bricks.

What did the last pig build his house with?

Which one is a dinosaur?

What part of our body do we use to smell?

Which room has the potty?

What are these parts of our hands?

Which one is a dinosaur?

What part of our body do we use to smell?

Nose

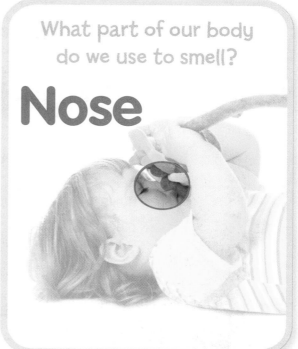

Which room has the potty?

What are these parts of our hands?

Fingers

Read the story, then answer the question.

Goldilocks and the Three Bears

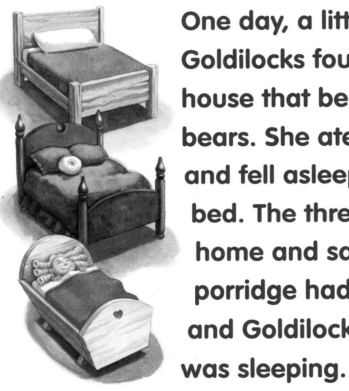

One day, a little girl named Goldilocks found an empty house that belonged to three bears. She ate their porridge and fell asleep in Baby Bear's bed. The three bears came home and saw that their porridge had been eaten and Goldilocks was sleeping.

Goldilocks woke up, saw the bears, and ran away as fast as she could!

Where did Goldilocks fall asleep?

Read the story, then answer the question.

Goldilocks and the Three Bears

One day, a little girl named Goldilocks found an empty house that belonged to three bears. She ate their porridge and fell asleep in Baby Bear's bed. The three bears came home and saw that their porridge had been eaten and Goldilocks was sleeping. Goldilocks woke up, saw the bears, and ran away as fast as she could.

She fell asleep in Baby Bear's bed.

Where did Goldilocks fall asleep?

Questions

What is this called?

What time of year do we celebrate Halloween and Thanksgiving?

Which animal is black and white?

What is the opposite of dark?

DARK ____ **?**

What is this called?

Hair

What time of year do we celebrate Halloween and Thanksgiving?

Fall

Which animal is black and white?

Skunk

What is the opposite of dark?

DARK LIGHT

Read the story, then answer the question.

Snow White

There once was a wicked queen with a magic mirror. It said that Snow White was more beautiful than the queen. Snow White was scared, so she ran into the forest, where she found seven dwarfs living in a cottage. One day, the queen tried to poison Snow White. But a prince saved her and they lived happily ever after.

How many dwarfs did Snow White find in the forest?

Read the story, then answer the question.

Snow White

There once was a wicked queen with a magic mirror. It said that Snow White was more beautiful than the queen. Snow White was scared, so she ran into the forest, where she found seven dwarfs living in a cottage. One day, the queen tried to poison Snow White. But a prince saved her and they lived happily ever after.

She found 7 dwarfs.

How many dwarfs did Snow White find in the forest?

Questions

Which animal lives in a tree?

What are these parts of our feet?

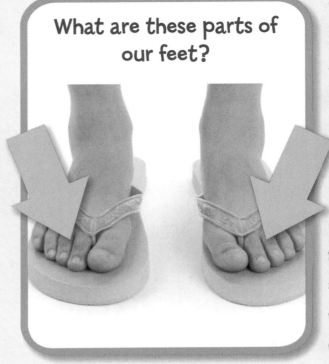

What do we use to taste?

What do we say if we hurt someone's feelings?

Which animal lives in a tree?

Owl

What are these parts of our feet?

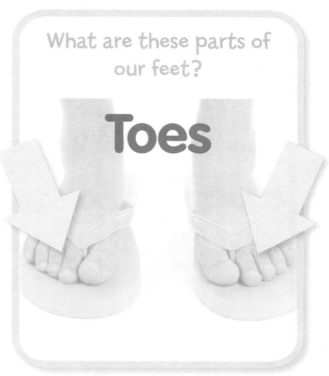

Toes

What do we use to taste?

Tongue

What do we say if we hurt someone's feelings?

I'm sorry

Read the story, then answer the question.

Rapunzel

Once there was an evil witch who had a very tall tower. She kept Rapunzel locked up in the tower. Rapunzel had very long hair. One day, a handsome prince found Rapunzel and climbed up her hair to the tower. Then he helped her escape and they lived happily ever after.

Where did Rapunzel live?

Read the story, then answer the question.

Rapunzel

Once there was an evil witch who had a very tall tower. She kept Rapunzel locked up in the tower. Rapunzel had very long hair. One day, a handsome prince found Rapunzel and climbed up her hair to the tower. Then he helped her escape and they lived happily ever after.

Where did Rapunzel live?

She lived in a tower.

Questions

What do we use to eat our food?

What is the opposite of up?

UP   **?**

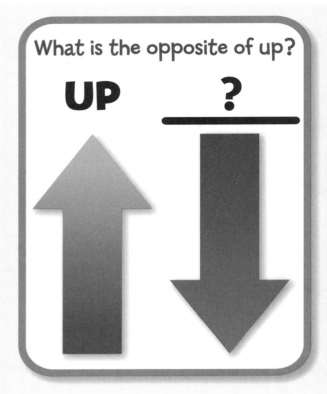

What do we say when we are leaving?

Which animal lives on a farm?

What do we use to eat our food?

Mouth

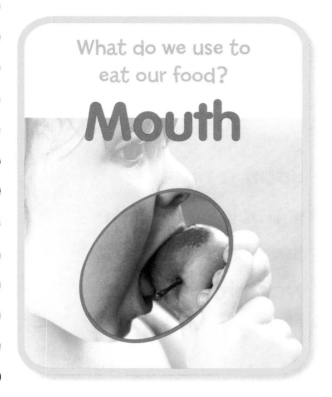

What is the opposite of up?

UP **DOWN**

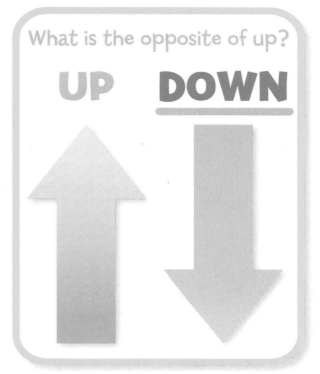

What do we say when we are leaving?

Good-bye

Which animal lives on a farm?

Goat

Read the story, then answer the question.

The Ugly Duckling

Once upon a time, a mother duck had some baby ducklings. One of them was big and gray. Everyone teased him.

One day, the ugly ducking saw a beautiful swan. He wanted to be beautiful, too. Over time, the sad and lonely ugly duckling grew into what he always was: a swan! No one teased him anymore.

What did the ugly duckling grow up to become?

Read the story, then answer the question.

The Ugly Duckling

Once upon a time, a mother duck had some baby ducklings. One of them was big and gray. Everyone teased him.

One day, the ugly ducking saw a beautiful swan. He wanted to be beautiful, too. Over time, the sad and lonely ugly duckling grew into what he always was: a swan! No one teased him anymore.

He grew up to be a swan.

What did the ugly duckling grow up to become?

Questions

What number comes next?

3 4 __

Which one starts with the letter **R**?

Are there more birds or fish?

What letter comes next?

DE __

What number comes next?

3 4 5

6

Which one starts with the letter **R**?

Ring

Are there more birds or fish?

Birds

What letter comes next?

D E F

Questions

Which ball is on the left?

What letter comes next?

What colors are in the rainbow?

Which rhymes with bat?

Which ball is on the left?

What letter comes next?

What colors are in the rainbow?

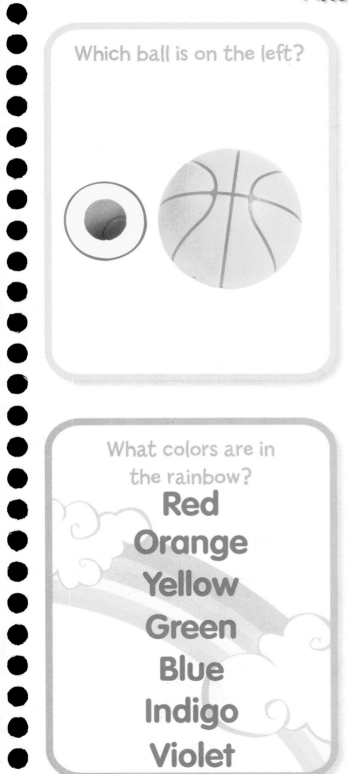

Red
Orange
Yellow
Green
Blue
Indigo
Violet

Which rhymes with bat?

Cat

178

Questions

Where do we wear shoes?

What is the correct order of these pictures?

Which begins with the letter **E**?

Which word starts the same way as cow?

Where do we wear shoes?

On our feet

What is the correct order of these pictures?

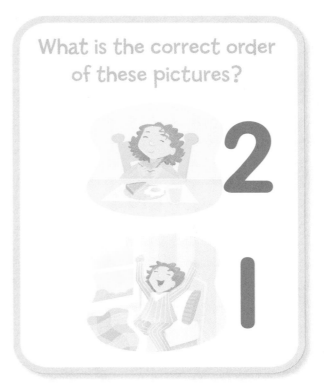

2

1

Which begins with the letter **E**?

Elephant

Which word starts the same way as cow?

Cup

Questions

What shape is the button?

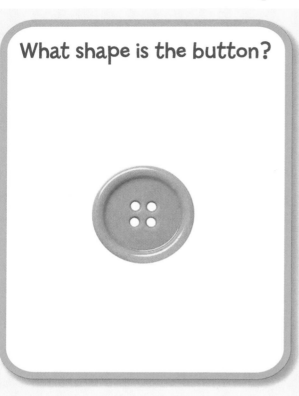

Which word starts the same way as ball?

How many oranges are there?

Which one is black?

What shape is the button?

Circle

Which word starts the same way as ball?

Boat

How many oranges are there?

13

Which one is black?

Which two words rhyme?

dog

duck

frog

How many sides does this shape have?

Which person is taller?

Who helps us when there's a fire?

Which two words rhyme?

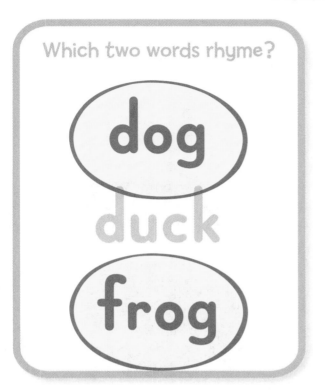

dog

duck

frog

How many sides does this shape have?

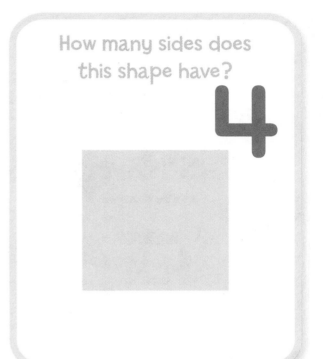

4

Which person is taller?

COACH

Who helps us when there's a fire?

Firefighters

Questions

Where would we find books?

Who keeps people safe?

How many squares do you see?

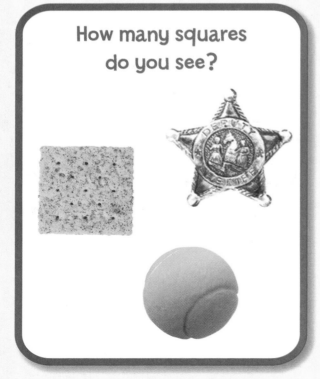

Where do we buy food?

Where would we find books?
Library
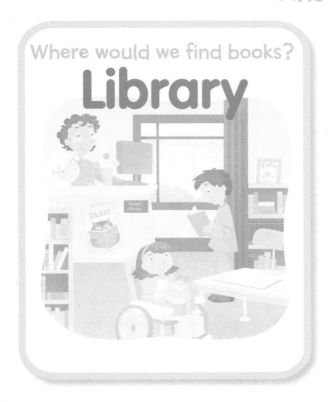

Who keeps people safe?
Police Officer

How many squares do you see?
I
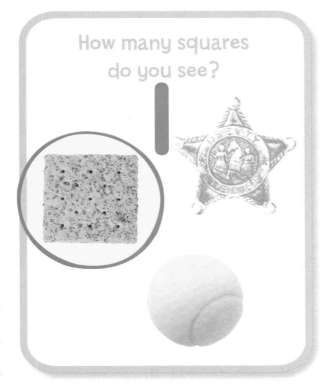

Where do we buy food?
Grocery store

Questions

How many dots are on the domino?

Which is lowercase **A**?

a c u

How many circles are in this pair of glasses?

Which of these grows on a tree?

Answers

How many dots are
on the domino?

5

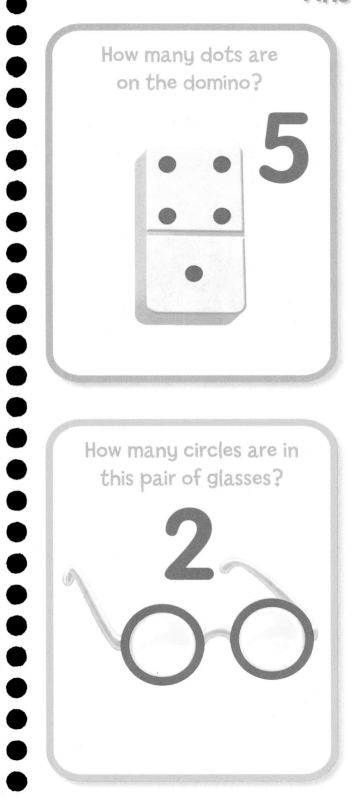

Which is lowercase **A**?

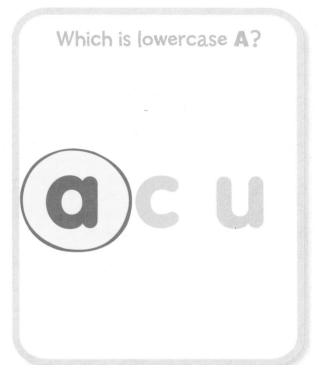

How many circles are in
this pair of glasses?

2

Which of these grows
on a tree?

Apple

Questions

Which animal jumps?

When the traffic light is red, what do we do?

Which two words rhyme?

cat

bat

orange

Which starts with the letter **G**?

Which animal jumps?

Kangaroo

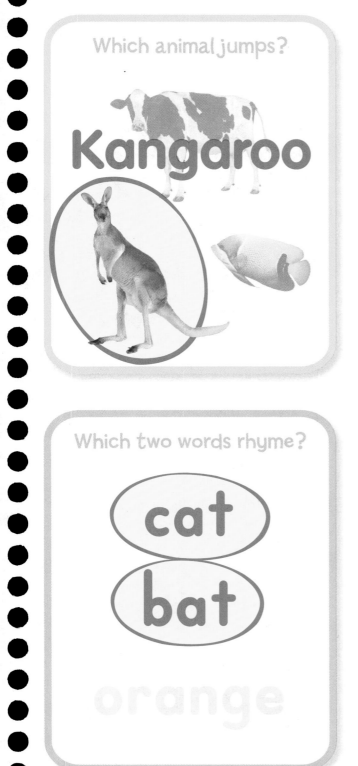

When the traffic light is red, what do we do?

Stop

Which two words rhyme?

cat

bat

orange

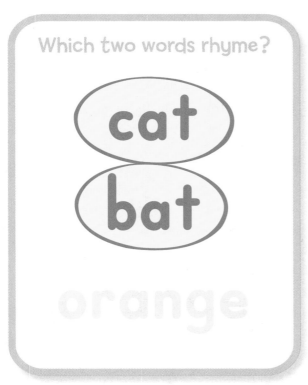

Which starts with the letter **G**?

Goat

Questions

Which would we wear in the summer?

Which one is a purple diamond?

What should we always wear in the car?

In an emergency, what number should we dial?

Answers

Which would we wear in the summer?

Which one is a purple diamond?

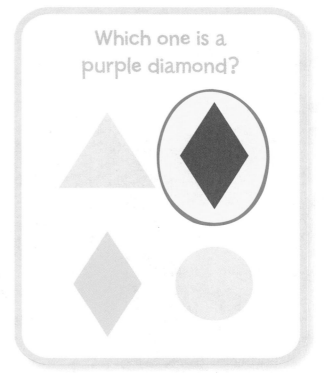

What should we always wear in the car?

Seat belt

In an emergency, what number should we dial?

911